Mary, Quite Contrary

Mary, Mary, quite contrary,
How does your garden grow?
With silver bells and cockleshells,
And pretty maids all in a row.

Mary planted some seeds.

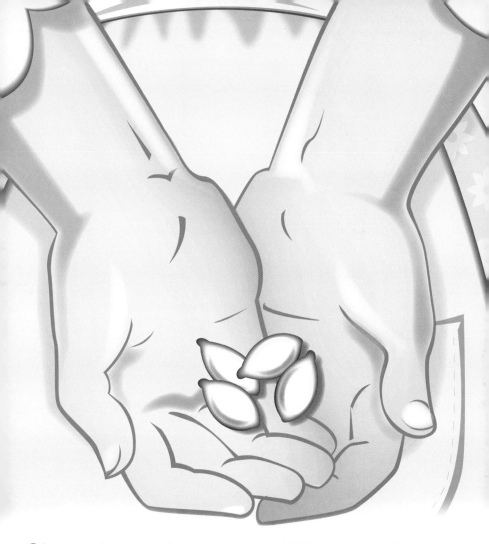

She planted some white seeds...

then orange pumpkins grew.

4

She planted some black seeds...

then yellow sunflowers grew.

She planted some red seeds
and some brown seeds...

then a big, green beanstalk grew!